Alan

EVERYTHING YOU NEED TO KNOW WHEN YOU'RE

WHEN YOU'RE

Piccadilly Press • London

*Best wishes to Laura and Samuel,
and thanks to Darren, Lisa and Eric
(who are seven at heart!)*

Text copyright © Alan Dapré, 1996

Designed by Lisa Nutt and Kit.
Printed and bound by Progressive Printing Ltd., Leigh-on-Sea
for the publishers Piccadilly Press Ltd.,
5 Castle Road, London NW1 8PR

A catalogue record for this book is available from the British
Library

ISBN: 1 85340 372 5 (hardback)
1 85340 377 6 (paperback)

Alan Dapré lives in Nottingham, where he works as a primary
school teacher. He has written several books, and plays for
Radio Four. He was a winner of the 1991 Radio 4's Young
Playwrights Festival.

Other books in the series:
EVERYTHING YOU NEED TO KNOW WHEN YOU'RE NINE
EVERYTHING YOU NEED TO KNOW WHEN YOU'RE EIGHT
'Carries sublime insights' – Observer

CONTENTS
Introduction

Introduction

This book is specially written for when you are seven. **WARNING!** It is not suitable for all seven-year-olds. Please do not put it anywhere near:

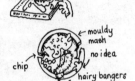

- a **seven**-year-old pet dog,

or

- a **seven**-year-old school dinner!

BEFORE YOU READ ON:
TYPE YOUR AGE ON THE KEY PAD BELOW
THEN PRESS ENTER

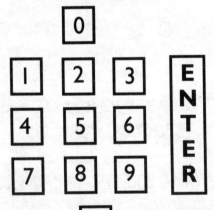

If you pressed button 7 then **CONGRATULATIONS!**
Turn to the next page (and skip page 7).
If you pressed any other buttons then **OH DEAR!**
Tomorrow morning you will get a terrible

S.H.O.C.K.
Turn to page 7 to discover what it is.

SUPER-SEVEN-YEAR-OLDS

HOW SUPER ARE YOU?

To find out if you are a super seven-year-old try this quick quiz:

1. *When you go to school do you*
a) walk slowly?
b) go by car?
c) fly?

2. *On school days do you get changed*
a) ultra slowly so you are late for school?
b) when your parents tell you to?
c) in a telephone box?

3. *When school dinners are dished out do you*
a) eat yours slowly and play with it?
b) have sandwiches instead?
c) scoff it at super-speed so you can spend more time in the not-so-super playground?

1

4. *At home time do you*

a) spend ages in the cloakroom putting your coat on?
b) forget to take home your reading book?
c) leave school at the speed of light?

5. *Are your favourite sweets*

a) so hard boiled they crack your teeth?
b) gobstoppers (you stop talking for a year)?
c) extra-strong mints?

Super hot breath

Super hot mints

What did you choose?

Mostly a's – You're about as super as a seven-year-old sock.

Mostly b's – Read everything in this book and you will soon be a super-seven-year-old.

Mostly c's – You are a real **SUPERSTAR.** (Top tip! Don't wear your underwear on the outside. It's so uncool!)

HOW TO SPOT A SUPER SEVEN-YEAR-OLD

Super seven-year-olds have **SUPER HEARING** so they always know what Mum and Dad are whispering about.

Have you noticed that parents always whisper when they are trying to keep things a secret?

They talk quietly when they don't want you to know that all your birthday presents are on top of the wardrobe, or in the loft.

They also whisper when they don't want to wake you up (because they are eating yummy things like chocolate and crisps).

Super seven-year-olds can **FLY** – at supersonic speed. Which means that they go so fast they make a loud **booming** sound. Mums and dads also make loud booming sounds when they see seven-year-olds flying around the house.

Many seven-year-olds have a secret identity so people will not guess that they are so super. Super seven-year-olds walk around school looking just like everyone else.

However, when they hear a cry for help they will dash into the nearest phone box (or lunch-box) and come out in a super outfit – which looks something like this:

Super seven-year-olds have relatives with super powers too!

Super Granny

(the fastest knitter in the world)

Super Grandpa

(weeds the garden in just seven seconds)

It is a fact that really super seven-year-olds do nice things for people.

They take animals out for a walk.

They help little old ladies cross the road.

Sometimes their special **super powers** can get them into trouble (even on a birthday).

Of course, not every seven-year-old is super. What do you think of these seven-year-olds? *(Not much – Ed.)*

a) a seven-year-old haircut

b) a seven-year-old blob of chewing gum

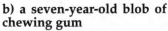

c) a seven-year-old party invitation

d) a seven-year-old joke*

*Teachers love to tell rotten jokes. If you do not laugh (until your head falls off) they
a) write the joke on the blackboard.
b) make you learn it off by heart.

THE SEVEN <u>WORST</u> TEACHER JOKES EVER!

1) What shoes are made with banana skins?

- *Slippers*

2) How do bees make their hair look nice?

- *They use honeycombs*

3) What did one tomato say to the other?

- *Run ahead and I'll ketchup later*

4) Which snakes are good at sums?

- *Adders*

5) If your clock strikes thirteen what time is it?

- *Time to get a new clock*

6) When is a yellow book not a yellow book?

- *When it's read*

7) Why did the teacher wear sunglasses?

- *Because her pupils were so bright*

If you tell teachers your brilliant jokes they never laugh. If you are baffled by this just remember that teachers *only laugh at their own jokes!*

This book is only for seven-year-olds.
If you are not seven years old then:

Ha ha

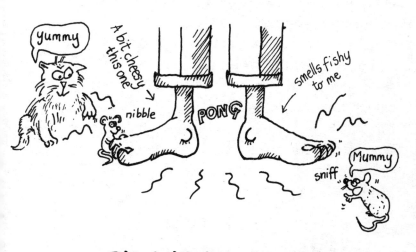

THE S.H.O.C.K. news is this.
When you wake up tomorrow morning
YOUR FEET WILL SMELL LIKE
<u>S</u>OME <u>H</u>ORRIBLE <u>O</u>LD <u>C</u>OOKED <u>K</u>IPPERS!

YOU HAVE BEEN WARNED!

The world is full of many other super-baffling things.

For instance, have you ever wondered ...
● Why dads wash their cars just before it rains?
● What the Tooth Fairy does with all the rotten teeth she collects?
● Why mums always pick a shopping trolley with wobbly wheels?
● Why only one sock comes out of the washing machine when you put two in?
● Why teenage brothers have small, hairy caterpillars stuck on their top lips?
● Why your gran thinks your best friend is much politer than you?

EVERYTHING YOU NEED TO KNOW ABOUT FUN WITH FRIENDS

Friends come in many shapes and sizes:

swotty friends   potty friends   snotty friends   spotty friends

BEST FRIENDS:

Mums like you to keep some clothes 'for best'. They can only be worn on special days like birthdays. Best clothes usually cost a lot of money and are stored carefully away in a wardrobe until you want them. Best friends are not. Best friends should never be kept in a wardrobe or a chest of drawers because

a) they are afraid of the dark.

b) they will snore and keep you awake at night.

A best friend is easy to spot.

Best friends will:
● give you a sweet/toy/COLD when you haven't got one.
● let you come round to play (or tidy up).
● offer to swop things, e.g. two baby brothers for two hamsters!
● take your coat home from school, by mistake.
● miss you when you go on holiday (and go crazy when you forget to send them a postcard, or bring back a pressie).
● sometimes *drive you crazy*.

Best friends look like this

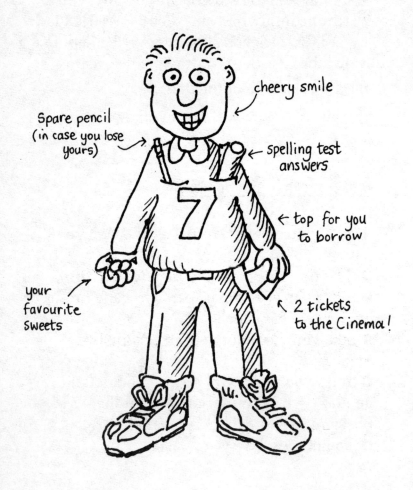

cheery smile

Spare pencil (in case you lose yours)

spelling test answers

top for you to borrow

your favourite sweets

2 tickets to the Cinema!

Best friends can also look like this!*

sulky frown (because you can't come out to play)

mud all over your 'best' trousers

* You see, best friends are not always sunny and smiley!

To be a best friend you don't have to be the best footballer in the school, or the best looking. You just have to be a **brilliant friend.** Sometimes best friends will make you want to stomp about and pull your hair out. Especially when they:

a) make your room a mess (and then go home).

BYE

b) take (or break) your toys.

c) fall in love with your sister (yuk!).

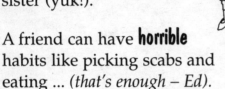

A friend can have **horrible** habits like picking scabs and eating ... *(that's enough – Ed)*.

WHICH OF THESE SEVEN HORRIBLE HABITS DO YOUR FRIENDS HAVE?

1. They get all your games out then go home for tea, and you have to put them all away.

2. They keep on saying what they are going to get for Christmas or their birthday.

3. They go straight to the biscuit tin or your computer when they come in.

4. They bring round loads of sweets when you're ill (then eat them all because you're too poorly to have any yourself).

5. They never invite you to their houses (even though they are ALWAYS round at yours).

6. They say dead creepy things to your parents like, 'I like your new haircut/dress/power drill'.

7. They never wipe their smelly noses or feet.

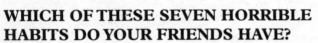

Lots of best friends row with each other and fall out. The trick is to make friends again as soon as you can. True friends will care for each other (deep down) and will not want to become worst enemies!

TYPES OF BEST FRIEND

There are three types of best friend. The *borrower*, the *basher* and the *beamer*.

Borrowers like coming round to your house, because they know you have lots of terrific toys that they can take home with them. *Borrowers* only borrow new toys. They won't touch anything that is broken, or dented. Sometimes *borrowers* will bring their grotty toys round and secretly swop them with your nice new ones. Then they pretend that they haven't done this! The only way to beat a *borrower* is to go round to his or her house and borrow back your own toys.

Bashers are very clumsy. As soon as they come into your bedroom they'll knock something over, like a bedside lamp or a mirror, and smash it into a zillion pieces. They might get seven years bad luck, but you'll get the blame (as usual) from Dad for 'leaving things in the way'. *Bashers* are not very good at taking care of your toys so *never* let them play with anything that costs a lot of money, or is new. *Bashers* only come round to your house to play with your toys because all of their toys are broken.

Beamers are very quiet and well behaved. They walk around your house with a beaming smile – from ear to ear. *Beamers* always play with your toys carefully. They never break them or borrow them. *Beamers* bring their brand new toys round to your house so you can play with them, and they don't mind if you keep them *for ever*.

Your best friend will probably be a bit of a *borrower* and a *basher*. And, of course, **YOU** are a *beamer*! *(I thought **beamers** didn't exist – Ed)*.

HOW TO BE A BRILLIANT BEST FRIEND

● Don't forget your friends' birthdays (even if they forget yours).

● If you give your friend a big present you shouldn't expect a big present back.

(Fab fact: A thousand years ago, white elephants were very popular 'big' presents, but you needed a big back garden and a lot of buns!)

● Join in with your friends' hobbies (if you always do different things then you won't see each other very often).

● Cheer your friends up when they feel sad.

Seven wacky ways friends can cheer you up

1. Friends let you splat them with custard pies.

2. Friends give you lots of hugs (okay ... as long as your friends aren't grizzly bears).

3. Friends help you eat your sandwiches (the ones you don't like).

4. Friends make funny faces (okay ... but Granny says they'll stay like that if the wind changes).

5. Friends say nice things to you – like 'Your clothes are lovely'. What they never say is, 'I'll do your homework for you'.

6. Friends send you notes. Friends always give you notes at the wrong time, e.g. just when you are about to do P.E. So you have to tuck the note into your sock and when you do a handstand it falls out, flutters on to the floor *in front of the teacher*, and you get into **BIG TROUBLE** (even bigger than a white elephant).

FINALLY!

7. Friends give you the things they find in their pockets, e.g.

- scrunched-up crisps
- half-sucked sweets
- sticky toffee covered in fluff
- squashed spiders
- old spelling lists

- bits of pencil rubber
- felt-tip lids
- old plasters
- school letters
- chewed fingernails

Furry, feathery & fishy friends

Friends don't have to be other kids. You can have animal friends too. (Isn't a kid a baby goat? Just kidding – Ed.) Why not choose furry friends, feathery friends or even fishy friends?

FURRY FRIENDS

Furry animals can be super friends. They are nice to hold, stroke or pat when you are feeling sad. Furry friends come in all shapes and sizes

some are a
tall shape

some are
a small shape

some are
a ball shape

Furry friends are usually small, round and squeaky (a bit like baby brothers and sisters) or they are large, bouncy and very very wet!

Furry dogs and cats need to be combed or brushed to get tangles out of their hair. They often grow a thick coat of fur for the winter. Then this hair falls out so they can stay cool in the summer. Some furry friends like to go on walks. Others (hamsters, gerbils) like to sit in the corner of their cages and sleep all day. Then all night they run on a squeaky wheel and keep you awake.

Cats make great lap-warmers in cold weather, however some seven-year-olds are allergic to furry animals, and sneeze or have a runny nose when they get too close to them. If this happens to you, why not have a feathery or fishy friend instead?

Top tip: Why not make your own fantastic furry pet that's guaranteed not to get up anyone's nose?

What you need:
- Grandpa's wig
- a dog collar and a lead
- sticky paper and a pen

1. Sneakily take Grandpa's wig off his head when he's not looking, or when he's asleep on the sofa (use a fishing rod).
2. Cut the sticky paper into circles and make them look like eyes.
3. Stick the 'eyes' on to the wig.
4. Put the collar on the wig and attach the lead.
5. Now take your fab furry pet for a walk and amaze your friends. *

* This (almost) perfect pet will: 'sit', 'stay' and 'lie down'. It will not 'fetch', 'heel' or 'beg'. It doesn't need food or water, just an occasional comb (and blob of hair cream).

FEATHERY FRIENDS

Budgies, canaries and parrots are popular feathery friends. Many feathery friends like you to talk to them, and some (parrots) even talk back.

a parrot
(makes a super pet)

a carrot
(not so super)

Many years ago, parrots were favourite friends of pirates. Mean, old pirates liked them because they were going cheep... sorry cheap. Parrots are famous for saying things like, 'Pieces of eight' and 'Who's a pretty boy then?' They are a bit sneaky because they like to repeat what you have just been saying. If you are in a room with a fast-talking feather-brained friend never say things like, 'Dad has smelly feet' or 'Mum has pongy perfume' because the parrot will tell them.

Instead, teach your parrot to say, **'Seven-year-olds should have more pocket money'** and **'Seven-year-olds should be allowed to go to bed when they want.'**

Pete Parrot has been in the front room listening to what Dad, Mum, Grandpa, baby brother, Rover (the dog) and Tiddles (the cat) have been saying. Can you work out who said what?

'Go and tidy your bedroom'

'Woof'

'Miaow'

'Give your gran a goodnight kiss'

'WAAAHHH!!!!'

'Slurp slurp'*

* translated as 'Now where did I put my false teeth?'

FISHY FRIENDS

Fish are very good at swimming, and er...
blowing bubbles. Fishy friends can be all the
colours of the rainbow. Tropical fish like
warm water and they enjoy swimming in
large glass tanks. Never keep your fish in a
small bowl, because it can be v. boring
swimming in circles all day. (And it's pretty
boring to look at too). If you have a fish tank,
give your fish plenty of interesting things to
swim round, and lots of places to hide.

Small water snails help keep fish tanks
clean (they eat the green slimy stuff that
grows on the glass). A light and a pump will
also give your fishy friends a bright and bubbly home. If you like the idea of having a
tank of fishy friends (but you don't want the
fuss of looking after them) why not try this
top tip?

1. Take a see-through plastic ice-cream tub.
2. Eat all the ice-cream!
3. Fill your tank with sand and water.
4. Peel a carrot, drop the peelings into
   the water.

HEY PRESTO ... an instant aquarium guaranteed to fool your friends! *(Sounds fishy to me – Ed.)*

Some seven-year-olds have fish ponds in their gardens. Ponds are **very dangerous places** so always take a grown-up with you when you go near one! Grown-ups can keep an eye on you, and they are very useful for carrying buckets, jam jars and nets!

FISH 'N' TIPS

If you keep your fishy friends in a pond:

- Remember to keep the water topped up.
- Try not to let your pond become clogged up with pond weed.
- Check there are no frog or toad eggs on the weed when it's removed.
- Don't break any ice on the surface of the pond, or your fishy friends will get a thumping headache! Leave a plastic ball floating on the surface instead. It will let enough air into the water for your fish to survive until the warmer weather.

Many animals are soft, cuddly or pretty to look at. Some become invisible when they are in trouble (just like naughty brothers and sisters). This trick is called *camouflage.* An octopus can change colour so it looks like the sand on the sea bed. A chameleon (a kind of lizard) also changes colour to match the things around it. Some animals (stoats) grow a white winter coat so they can't be seen in the snow. Leopards have big spots so they can't be seen hiding in long grass. Funnily enough, big sisters use vanishing cream to make their spots disappear.

Seven-year-olds have a few tricks of their own too.

VANISHING TRICK ONE

When being growled at by a grizzly Dad, start hopping about on one leg, and say that you need the toilet. When you get into 'the smallest room in the house' pull out a copy of your favourite book (this one, of course!) from under the bath mat. Then spend ages reading it. By the time you come out Dad will

have forgotten that he was growling at you.
(Watch out there isn't a long queue outside
the door or you'll have all the rest of the
family grizzling like bears with sore heads.)

VANISHING TRICK TWO

When an ostrich is in trouble it will bury its
head in the sand until the danger has gone
away (well, that's what Dad says).
When you are in
trouble with
grown-ups,
bury your
head in your
hands and go,
'Boo hoo' loudly

(don't forget to squeeze out some crocodile
tears).With luck the grown-ups will think you
are really sorry about what you've done and
let you vanish outside to play.

CRAZY CAMPS & GOOFY GANGS

It is nice to have a camp that you can go and
play in:
a) away from **beastly** brothers and sisters.
b) away from your **world's worst** enemy.
c) away from **pesky** pets.

Indoors

Super camps can be built under the dining table. As soon as Mum or Dad put a table cloth on the table sneak under it, with your favourite toys and games. It's a great place to be when someone's having a party!

Make this periscope to get your hands on the grub before greedy brothers and sisters.

Why not turn your bedroom into a cool camp? Borrow all the pillows around the house and make your own tent using sheets or a duvet. Then pretend to be an undercover agent! Make sure a grown-up doesn't make the bed or you'll be trapped inside!

It's just as much fun making a camp under the bed, but watch out for slithery spiders, pongy old 'lost' socks, and grown-ups hoovering the carpet.

Cardboard boxes make super camps. Ask your parents if they can go and buy a new fridge so that you can have the huge box that it is delivered in. You can paint a big box to look like a bus, or cover it with signs to warn non-seven-year-olds to keep away!

Ask a friendly grown-up to cut look-out holes for you so you can see if any enemy spies are raiding the new fridge.

WARNING: Make sure you do not get parcelled up and sent to a faraway place like TIMBUKTU or MARGATE.

Here's another easy way to make a camp. All you need is a skipping rope, an old sheet, two chairs and a cream cake.

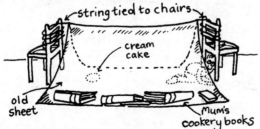

When you have made your camp, crawl inside and eat the cream cake. Simple, huh?

As you can see, there are oodles of ways to make camps. Here are some more places you can explore.

● Behind the sofa – beware of yukky things that the cat has hidden there.

● In the bath – beware of drippy brothers turning the taps on.

● Under the stairs – beware of the dark!!!

● In the spare room – beware of old boxes, Dad's brand new (untouched) exercise bike, and ... gulp ... **more spiders.**

Outdoors

If you have a garden then you will find lots of great hiding places where you can make a camp.

in bushes   in a hollow tree

in corners  in a shed

Top tip: It is not a good idea to make a camp

● in a hole – you might not be able to climb out, or see creepy crawlies climbing up your leg!

● up a tree – you might get stuck up there like next door's cat, or fall out!

In story-books, gangs of seven-year-olds often meet in a garden shed. Sheds can be good camps because they are warm, dry and at the bottom of the garden so you can't hear Mum telling you it's time:
– for your friends to go home.
– for your cough medicine.
– for bed.

In stories, a gang will have a shiny clean shed with tables, chairs and cupboards crammed full of yummy sweets and fizzy drinks.

Sadly, in real life ... sheds are crammed with old junk that used to belong to your great-great-great-great grandparents. So you'll have to clear out old bicycles and huge typewriters, plus cracked paddling pools, boxes full of smelly wellington boots, rusty tricycles and dangerous kid-eating deck-chairs.

If you start your own gang there are Seven Golden Rules.

Rule 1: GIVE YOUR GANG A NAME

Easy, this – simply count the number of seven-year-olds in your gang and call yourselves *The Terrific Three*, *The Top Two* or *The ... er ... Wonderful One!* If your gang wants to save the planet why not be called *The Environmental Eight* or *The Green Fingers Gang?* If you can't think of a catchy name why not call it *The Gang?*

Rule 2: HAVE A PASSWORD

If your gang meets up in the dark, in disguise, or when it's foggy then it's a good idea to have a password (top tip: make sure only kids in the gang know what the password is). When someone mysterious comes up to you and says, 'Seven' (the password) you will know that it is a friend.

Or why not have two passwords that link up? If the person says, 'Fish' you will say, 'Chips'. Here are some more:

'Bangers' + 'Mash'; 'Sun' + 'Moon'; 'New' + 'Old'; 'Salt' + 'Pepper'; 'Pen' + 'Paper'; 'Up' + 'Down'.

You could learn a poem instead of a password, or why not create your own crazy sentences?

Rule 3: HAVE A PLACE TO MEET

You can easily turn your bedroom into a gang headquarters (HQ). A bedroom is a super place to meet (especially if you do not have a shed). Put posters on your walls, with drawings of the gang on them and set up booby traps to keep spies away.

Watch out if you have to share it with someone who is not in your gang (e.g. a baby brother or sister). They might steal all your secrets or set up a rival gang.

Meeting friends at school is not much fun, because you only see each other in the wet and windy playground. Cloakrooms are much warmer, but watch out for **stinky** P.E. kits and **stinky** monitors who will spy on you and tell the teachers.

Rule 4: KEEP YOUR GANG A SECRET

If all the boring kids (non-seven-year-olds)
find out you have a gang they will want to
join it, and you'll soon be so bored you'll
have to leave and start up another one!

Rule5: MAKE A CATCHPHRASE

The Three Musketeers used to shout out 'All
for one, and one for all.' If one of them was in
trouble the other musketeers (French soldiers)
would come to the rescue. A catchphrase tells
people what the gang is about. Have fun
making up your own crazy catchphrases, like
these: 'Who shares wins'; 'The Good, the
Bad, and the Cuddly'.

Rule 6: HAVE A MASCOT

Dogs make marvellous
mascots, but any
pet will do. A
mascot should
bring the gang
good luck. But
if you've got
a dog it will
probably bring
you a bone
instead.

Rule 7: HAVE AT LEAST ONE FRIEND WHO
WANTS TO JOIN
If no one wants to join
your gang then either
join another gang or
take your mascot for
a walk.

a dogfish?

(What if it's a fish? – Ed.)

Press Gangs

About 200 years ago, many sailors did not
want to sail on Royal Navy ships because
they were so bad. The food was horrid, and
they were full of **rats!** By law, men could be
made to sail on these ships, even when they
didn't want to. Gangs armed with cutlasses
(curved swords) would grab men off the
street and carry them back to their ships,
which then sailed out to sea. These unwilling
sailors would not get back home for years.
They were 'pressed' into service for up to
five years.

If you don't fancy being in a gang then don't
be in one. If other kids try to make you join
either walk away, or say you're already in a
gang but you can't say which one because
it's a secret. If they still pester you, don't be
afraid to tell a grown-up (e.g. a teacher or
your parents).

EVERYTHING YOU NEED TO KNOW ABOUT SURPRISES

Seven-year-olds love surprises. Some surprises are better than other surprises. ✓ or **X** which of these <u>surprises you would love to find</u>:

a worm in your apple ☐

spooks in the shed ☐

a slug in your salad ☐

pennies under your pillow ☐

buried treasure in your garden ☐

a spot on your nose ☐

Birthday surprises

Many seven-year-olds have birthday parties at home. But if you want to surprise your friends why not take them

- *swimming, skating or ten-pin bowling.*
- *on a picnic.*
- *back to school.* Have your party in the Hall so you can invite the whole class … and the school teachers/dinner ladies/hamsters!

Make your party surprising by:
- asking everyone to come dressed up as *fruit* or *pop stars.*

Or as

the Romans   space aliens   their pet

food   famous people   the weather

Perhaps your friends have to wear only red, or all dress the same?

PARTY INVITATIONS

Sometimes mums and dads pick who can come to the party. They ask all *their* friends to come, worse luck. Then they munch all the party food when you and your pals are playing games.

Grown-ups eat this

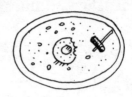

You and your friends eat this

If you are having a party always be careful about who you invite. Or you will end up with

• all your brother's and sister's rotten friends *who will cheat at Pass the Parcel and sulk if they don't win Musical Chairs.*

• your next door neighbours' kids *who will borrow your new football and kick it over the fence into their garden (and you'll never get it back).*

• the child minder. *Most child minders are lovely and will be great fun at parties. But watch out because some love to make you go into the kitchen to finish off your curly egg sandwiches (left over from school dinner time).*

There are some people you have to invite.

DADS...

will always put on a silly hat and try to win all the party games or sit in a corner and eat all the prizes. Dads can be embarrassing because they dance like this:

the funky chicken   the twist   the Egyptian

A dad will waltz around with you and swing you in the air until
a) you turn green.
b) his back goes 'click'.

When dads play music they will sing along to the words. Trouble is, they don't know all of them so they make the words up as they go along!

35

MUMS...

will spend hours getting everything ready.
They know all your friends' first, last and
middle names. When they arrive mums whip
away your presents before you get a chance to
open them. Mums walk around dishing out
jelly and ice-cream (but only if you are sitting
still), and pick chocolate buttons off the top of
small cakes.

When you play games mums tell dads to
stop being silly. When the party is over they
stand by the door holding all the kids' coats,
and give out party bags full of popped balloons and cakes (which have chocolate buttons
missing!).

BIG BROTHERS...

will go out if you have a party because they
think parties are babyish. Really, they would
love to be at your party but they worry what
their friends would say the next day at school.

BIG SISTERS...

stay at home but they won't eat any party
food (because they say it's full of additives
and E numbers). They will sit and sulk
because their favourite programme is on the
television and they are not allowed to watch it.

LITTLE BROTHERS AND SISTERS...

cry when they are not allowed to open your presents. They are always out first when you play Musical Statues. You always know where they are because they leave a trail of crumbs on the floor behind them.

GRANS...

sit in a corner, wearing a paper hat and a napkin on their laps. Dads won't let them play Musical Statues because grans beat them. (Grans move so slowly they always win.)

GRANDADS...

will play party music VERY LOUDLY so that all the food shakes off the plates and tables on to the floor. Some Grandads will hide bits of birthday cake in flower pots because the icing is too hard for their teeth.

COUSINS...

run all over the house and end up in your bedroom. Then they start playing with your new presents, or hiding in your cupboards.

THE CAKE

Birthday cakes are made in all shapes and sizes. Here's what they look like if:

you like football   *you like running*

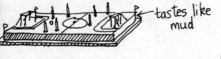

← tastes like mud

← tastes like an old boot!

you like T.V.   *you like school*

← tastes of soap

← tastes like school dinners

Top tip: Try to keep pets away from your birthday cake unless your big sister has made it!

Sometimes you may be given a cake that is dead embarrassing!

HAPPY BIRTHDAY TO OUR LITTLE BUNNY

So the secret is to tell the person who is making it (or buying it) exactly what you want it to look like, and taste like.

BIRTHDAY PRESENTS

Here are some presents that a seven-year-old received from her family. Can you guess who gave what?

PALS' PARTIES

If you are invited to a pal's seventh birthday party why not take along a home-made birthday card?

Then write a poem to go inside, e.g.

Roses are red,
Tomatoes are too.
Today you are seven
So I've made this for you!

If you have a present for your pal make sure it is:

a) not left at home on the kitchen table.

b) not something your friend bought for you on your birthday.

WRAPPING PRESENTS

It is not easy wrapping presents. Even a simple box can be hard to wrap. So get Mum to wrap your present, or hand it over when there is a power cut.

Guess the wrapped present

You can make your presents look pretty by tying them up with coloured string or bright ribbons.

UNWRAPPING PRESENTS

Grans always put lots of sticky tape on your present so it takes hours to get the paper off. You are so glad to get it open you don't mind if the present is rotten (another pair of itchy gloves).

CHOOSING WHAT TO WEAR

● Wear clothes with pockets so if you win any prizes you have somewhere safe to put them.

● If you wear a long party dress or baggy trousers be careful, or you might trip and get the bumps.

● Don't wear your favourite old clothes (e.g. ripped jeans with dirty knees) or Mum will go bonkers.

● Never wear the same clothes as your birthday pal.

● Never look prettier than the birthday girl or birthday boy. If you do then your friend
a) won't speak to you all day or
b) will drop ice-cream all over you 'by accident'.

PARTY BAGS

When the party is over seven-year-olds will often be given a party bag. It is meant to be filled with goodies. Trouble is, you will get this stuff instead, worse luck!

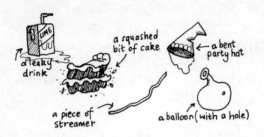

WHAT TO DO IF YOU ARE NOT INVITED

There's only one thing you can do. **Sulk.** Then get your own back when it is your next birthday (tee hee).

PARTY GAMES

Party games are great fun to play. Some silly seven-year-olds want to win all the games. If they lose they will sulk and stomp about (so they look even sillier). They forget that a party game is only a game, and that the prizes are never mega-expensive.

If you win you will get a bar of squashed chocolate or a balloon that is impossible to blow up. You never win a television or a new bike so it is not worth making a big fuss if you lose.

BUT: always let birthday boys or girls win one game (because it is their party and they might send you home without any tea!).

PARTY FOOD

Some seven-year-olds always eat too much party food and go home with a tummy ache and a green face. Other seven-year-olds always put piles of food on their plates, take one bite and leave the rest.

YOUR BIRTHDAY

Do you know what day you were born on? Was it a Friday or a Monday? Your mum or dad should be able to tell you. Why not find out and then read this poem:

Monday's child does lots of skips
Tuesday's child is full of chips
Wednesday's child likes heaps of snow
Thursday's child outside won't go
Friday's child works hard at school
Saturday's child is really cool
And the child who is born on Bath Day
Is bright and bubbly (well, that's what they say).

SCHOOL SURPRISES

If you go into a school today you're sure of a big surprise. One day, after your seventh birthday you will leave the infants and go into the junior school. In the junior school there are two types of teachers. **Cuddly** Teddy Bear teachers and growly **Grizzly** Bear teachers.

Teddy Bear Teachers

If you fall over they will give you a cuddle. In the summer they take all the kids in the class to the woods to have a picnic. When they were little they went to Cubs. **Teddy Bear teachers** like to call you 'Honey'. Their favourite story is *The Three Bears*. In the morning before school starts they go for a long walk in the woods while the porridge cools down.

a bun

another bun

Wrapped up for Winter

Their favourite joke is:
What do teddy bears have for breakfast
-Teddied Wheat

Their worst habit is that they forget to lock the front door when they go out for a walk.

Grizzly Bear Teachers

These are very scary. They have big hands (sorry, paws) and huge whiskery chins.
Grizzly Bear Teachers walk around school shouting, 'Someone's been sleeping in my classroom!' They never miss a thing.

They have a super sense of hearing so they know when you are secretly unwrapping a sweet.

Grizzlies never smile, except when they are eating porridge sandwiches or telling off naughty children. They can't bear rotten jokes. You can make them stop grizzling if you show them these super things:

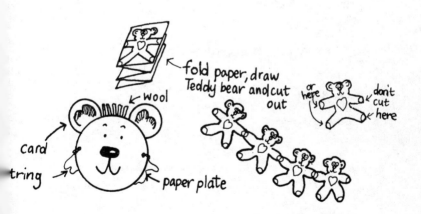

SURPRISE TESTS

Teachers love tests. They like to give seven-year-olds tricky problems such as this one:

A boy and his sister go for a walk with a dog called Rover. The boy is half the age of his sister who is twice the age of the dog. Rover is seven years old. How far did they walk?

Why not get your own back and surprise your teacher with this tricky spelling test?

Read the words to your teacher. Make sure your teacher cannot secretly peek at them.

1. **banister**
2. **desiccated**
3. **definite**
4. **accommodation**
5. **omnivorous**
6. **skilful**
7. **separate**

*Why not ask your teacher to say a word that begins with **und** and ends with **und**. (The word is ‘underground’.)*

More school surprises

School is full of surprises. You may see a surprise visitor (Nora the nit nurse), or you may have a surprise when you open your lunchbox (oops … it has no lunch inside). You may have a surprise school trip to a pencil factory. Will any of these surprising things happen at your school?

1) Your teacher lets you have the day off.

2) You are allowed to sing pop songs in assembly.

3) All the kids in your class bring in their P.E. kits.

4) The playground has lots of new swings and slides in it.

5) Your school footy team wins the World Cup. Twice.

6) Your school dinner tastes fab.

7) The caretaker gets your ball off the roof.

8) You discover your teacher is a mummy.

9) You get a part in the school play.*

*THE SCHOOL PLAY

NATIVITY PLAYS

Lots of schools have a Nativity Play at Christmas.

Most teachers like every child to act in the play. As there are only three kings, a few shepherds and one inn-keeper most of the kids have to be sheep, donkeys and kids (baby goats). It is the only time when teachers let you act like little animals.

The parts

You can only be a shepherd if your mum has an old sheet that she does not mind cutting up (for your costume).

If you are lucky you will get the part of an angel. They have to look very sweet and jump in the air a lot (to make it look like they are flying). Angels spend a lot of time hoping their wings won't fall off.

Some seven-year-olds want to play the part of Mary because she has a ride on a donkey. Sadly, most schools don't have real donkeys. They use one of these:

The three kings are good to play. They have to walk very slowly so that they do not trip over their cloaks. The three kings have to carry big presents. They have to make sure they don't drop them on a sheep, or in the manger.

If you are bright you can be the star and sit on top of the stable. If you are very bright you will have to learn everybody's lines, just in case someone is away when the play is put on.

PANTOMIMES

Some schools put on a pantomime. *Jack and the Beanstalk* and *Cinderella* are pantomimes. A panto has lots of bad jokes. The goodies (Jack, Cinderella) always win and beat the baddies (the Giant, Ugly Sisters).

Jack and the Beanstalk:

It is fun to play Jack because you get to climb a beanstalk *(it's a rubber plant – Ed)* and fight a giant *(it's the caretaker – Ed)*.

Jack has lots of adventures and at the end of the pantomime he is very rich. If you suffer from hay fever or do not like heights then why not be the cow or one of the magic beans instead?

Cinderella:

Cinderella should go to the ball in a golden carriage, pulled by six white horses. In school pantos she goes to the Hall in a shopping trolley, pulled by the school hamsters!

The best bit about being Cinderella is that you have a fairy godmother who will give you lots of wishes. The worst bits are that you have to clean out the fireplace, and you are nagged by the Ugly Sisters. Plus the Prince is always spotty and picks his nose.

THE TEACHER'S DESK

Surprise surprise. Teachers of seven-year-olds like to have large desks in their classrooms. On top you will see dirty coffee mugs and lots of apples. Every desk has a drawer which says:

KEEP OUT TEACHERS ONLY!

So if you have ever wondered what teachers keep in their drawers here is a sneaky secret look!

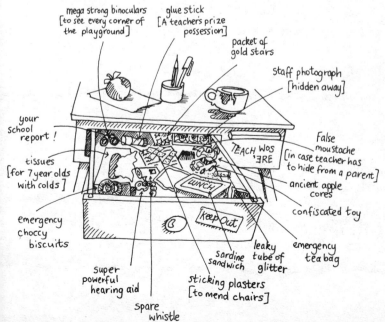

mega strong binoculars
[to see every corner of the playground]

glue stick
[A teacher's prize possession]

packet of gold stars

staff photograph
[hidden away]

your school report!

tissues
[for 7 year olds with colds]

false moustache
[in case teacher has to hide from a parent]

ancient apple cores

confiscated toy

emergency choccy biscuits

emergency tea bag

sardine sandwich

leaky tube of glitter

sticking plasters
[to mend chairs]

super powerful hearing aid

spare whistle

TEACH WOS 'ERE

LUNCH

Keep Out

SCHOOL REPORTS

A school report is written by your teacher and it tells your parents how you are getting on at school. School reports take a long time to write so teachers have invented new ways to write them.

The 'DO IT BY THE BOOK' method

A teacher will have a book full of things like, 'Sarah is a polite child who wears clean socks every day.' *The teacher opens the book, shuts his or her eyes, and jabs a pencil on one of the pages. Then the teacher writes down the sentence that the pencil landed on, e.g.* 'Sarah is good at taking away. Yesterday she took my whistle away and I haven't seen it since.'

The 'SECOND HAND' method

Your teacher blows the dust off a very old report that she or he wrote about sixty years ago. Then your teacher changes it a bit and makes it sound more modern. A second hand report looks like this:

Ye Olde Schoole Reporte

Sam ~~William~~ , verily, is a ~~lovelie~~ clever wonderful child. He has ~~ye goodly~~ manners.

He always asks if he may sharpen ye olde ~~quill~~ pencil and is very neat.

Written this day ~~in 1547~~

The 'CRAZY COMPUTER' method

The teacher puts your name into a computer and types in a lot of facts about you: your name, height, hobbies, favourite foods and best friend. The computer then makes up a report which looks a bit like this one:

WHIRR...CLICK...SARAH HAS BLUE EYES AND 370,000 BROWN HAIRS ON HER HEAD. SHE IS 107.5638292010 CENTIMETRES TALL. SARAH ENJOYS SWIMMING AND HAS 7 BADGES. SHE DOES NOT LIKE PRUNES AND CUSTARD. EVERY NIGHT SHE GOES TO 64 WALLABY LANE TO PLAY WITH HER BEST FRIEND CALLED ALBERT. ALBERT HAS TWO BROWN EYES AND 567,000 RED HAIRS ON HIS HEAD. HE IS ..........WHIRR...CLICK...

The 'DIY' method

All the teachers come into school and give every child a piece of blank paper. You are allowed half an hour to write your own school report. DIY reports look like this:

Brian is a brain-box and a genius. In fact, he is cleverer than all the teachers in the world put together. Last week he swam the Channel and the week before he won a gold medal at the Olympics. Even though he has had seven number one chart hits this term he still found time to sing in the school choir.

P.S. He is practically perfect in every way!

Mums and dads love to see good reports. If you have a rotten report **WATCH OUT!** At tea time:

a) your mum will blow up like a red hot volcano and steam will come out of her ears and nostrils. You will be sent to bed for 1,000 million years and not allowed to see your best friend again ... ever!

b) your dad will go mega-quiet, tap his fingers on the table then send you to bed for 1,000 million years, etc. etc. or

c) your mum and dad will talk quietly to each other when you are in bed and your pocket money will mysteriously disappear for ... ever!

Whatever happens, your brothers and sisters will nod at each other and snigger because you are in trouble.

WHAT TO DO IF YOU HAVE A ROTTEN REPORT

a) promise you will work hard and tidy up your bedroom every day (even if a grotty brother or sister has made all the mess).

b) say to your parents that there is someone in the class with the same name as you and that you took his/her report home by mistake.

c) look in all the dusty boxes in the attic and find your parents' old school reports. Then show them all the rotten bits!

WHAT TO DO IF YOU HAVE A REALLY GOOD REPORT

a) show it to all your brothers and sisters.

b) ask for more pocket money
(it won't work – Ed).

c) get out your parents' old school reports and see how well they did!

ALL TEACHERS WERE ONCE
SEVEN YEARS OLD

Next time you are in school take a peek at your teacher. Some teachers look wrinkly (like currants) and other teachers look crinkly (like crisps). It is amazing, but true, that ALL teachers have been seven years old. Of course, when your teacher was seven he or she looked just the same as he or she does now!

Your teacher aged seven   **Your teacher now**

Teachers have been around for a long, long time. Find out which of these things your teacher can remember!

☐ the first Moon landing (1969)
☐ the First World War (1914-1918)
☐ the Charge of the Light Brigade (1854)
☐ the last Ice Age
☐ the Ancient Greeks
☐ the New Seekers
☐ the Chopper (1970s bike)
☐ the Penny Farthing (1870s bike)
☐ the first pencil (1792)
☐ instant coffee invented (1938)
☐ the first hovercraft (1955)
☐ zip fastener invented (1891)

Count up the number of ticks. Now read on.

√√√√ = your teacher is a dinosaur.

√√√ = your teacher is crumblier than a digestive biscuit.

√√ = your teacher is not as old as you think.

Complete the following sentence:

I think my teacher is ☐ *years old.*

Show what you have written to your teacher ... if you dare!

SURPRISE VISITORS

During the school term schools are packed full of kids and the odd (very odd) teacher. During the school holidays schools are as crowded as Dracula's castle and twice as spooky.

The caretaker will potter about watering the plants and feeding the school hamster (which always escapes when its cage is opened and spends the holidays hiding in the Hall under the piano lid).

Visitors like to come to the school to have a look round. Sometimes the headteacher will take parents into classrooms so they can see

what the school is like. You always know
when this is about to happen because
teachers will spend all morning tidying up
their desks, or putting kids' work on the wall.

If a member of the Royal Family comes to
school the teachers will show you how to

a) curtsy or bow.

b) make a flag.

c) roll out a red carpet so it won't have
any bumps.

Famous writers come into schools to read
their stories and let you ask them questions,
like **'Do you chew your pencil?'** Other visitors, like
the school dentist or photographer also visit.

School dentists wear white coats and carry a mirror (so they can see what is at the back of your mouth). When the dentist comes into school you will have to line up and go in a small room. The dentist will have a peek at your teeth. If it is good news (and you don't have rotten teeth) the dentist will smile and write something down. If it is bad news (and you need fillings) then the dentist will smile and write something down.

In the past (up until 600 years ago) people only took your teeth out as a punishment. Many barbers (hairdressers) would have a go at being dentists. So if you went to a rotten barber (with good teeth) you could end up like this!

before   **after**

<u>School photographers</u> visit to take photographs of all the school children – usually when your hair is in a mess or just after you've spilt school gravy down your jumper. The photographer will also ask children to line up, often in the Hall. You then have your photo taken:

a) *by yourself*
Good points: you can sit on a comfy chair and miss a bit of school.
Bad points: you have to sit in front of a soppy picture of white clouds and blue sky. When the photographer says 'smile' and takes a photo the flash will dazzle you so you spend the rest of the day bumping into things. Or you will blink at the wrong time and look like you were asleep.

(NB: some photographers take so long to click the camera that you are asleep!)

FLASH!

b) *with brothers and sisters*
Good points: you will be able to laugh at them when you see the photo.

Bad points: they will be able to laugh at you! Plus they may fidget so much they knock you off the seat just as the camera goes click!

It is nice to keep old school photographs. You can see how much you have changed over the years:

aged 7

aged 10

aged 12

aged 14

1. BECOMING A MONITOR

Teachers like to ask pupils to help them by doing little jobs. These helpers (monitors) are chosen because they are

a) teacher's pets.

b) brilliant at everything they do.

Teachers will show you how to do your new job ... unless they have got you cleaning out the hamster/rabbit/skunk cage.

2. FINDING THINGS IN YOUR TRAY

Schools often give you a plastic tray to put your books in. This tray is always grey and has someone else's name stuck on the front. When you get given your tray it will be full of pencil shavings and bits of rubber.

Trays slide into wooden trolleys. When you put something in your tray it will fall down the back into the tray underneath. Trays are full of surprises. Inside you will find long lost gobstoppers and half-chomped packets of crisps, plus old football stickers, milk teeth and trillions of pencils this long:

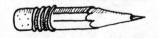

You will also find missing scissors, gerbils and notes. If you are given notes they will look like these:

3. MISSING COATS

It can be an awful surprise to find out your coat has gone. Coats have a strange habit of vanishing during the school day. You put a coat on your peg at the start of the day and by home-time it has gone forever. Either:

● your coat has been taken by another seven-year-old.
● your coat has been pinched by the caretaker.
● your coat has been pinched by space aliens.

Your coat will never be pinched by a seven-year-old because seven-year-olds do not put coats on when they go into the playground.

They would rather take a football or a skipping rope outside instead.

A caretaker won't make your coat vanish. Caretakers only make hot mugs of tea vanish, or kids who get too close to their super-sucky vacuum cleaners!

Your coat will have been taken by aliens from outer space. **Space aliens** love school coats because they think they look really cool in them!

Most school coats are very unfashionable. Many coats have hoods that bullies pull over your head, and pockets that are full of empty crisp packets.

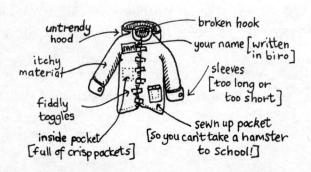

untrendy hood

broken hook

your name [written in biro]

itchy material

sleeves [too long or too short]

fiddly toggles

inside pocket [full of crisp packets]

sewn up pocket [so you can't take a hamster to school!]

THE MAGNIFICENT SEVEN

(Super seven facts to tell your friends)

● Sirius is the seventh nearest star to the planet Earth.

● The seventh planet in the solar system is Uranus. The planet Uranus is over 2,700 million kilometres from Earth!

● Manaslu 1 in Nepal is the seventh highest mountain in the world.

● The harvest mouse is the seventh smallest mammal in the world.

● Edward VII was king of England from 1901 to 1910.

● Australia is so large that it covers over seven million square kilometres.

● *Troilus and Cressida* is Shakespeare's seventh longest play.

● The film *Dances With Wolves* won seven Oscar awards.

● The emu lays between seven and sixteen eggs, which take about 60 days to hatch.

● The Beadlet Anemone is seven centimetres high and looks like a blob of jelly. When it is underwater lots of stinging tentacles open out to catch its dinner.

● The King Cobra is the seventh deadliest snake in the world. It can be nearly five metres long!

SURPRISES AT HOME

Surprising things happen at home too.

SURPRISE NUMBER ONE
An aunt comes to stay.
When it is bedtime she will sleep in your room and you'll end up:
a) in your baby brother or sister's room (and won't get any sleep because you're stuck in your old cot) or

b) in your older brother or sister's room (and won't get any sleep because older brothers and sisters SNORE!)*

*If you tell them they snore the next morning they will *never* believe you.

Aunts put their false teeth in your toothbrush mug. They always talk when your favourite T.V. shows are on. Or they knit very loudly. Aunts love cooking so they make you eat all the foods they like (such as haggis or asparagus). They cook lots of stringy beans and watery cabbage and dump it on your plate. Some days they don't wash the veg. so you will have creepy crawlies swimming in your gravy.

Uncles are just as bad. Uncles will arrive just when you are about to watch a cartoon and dump all their suitcases in front of the television. They tell you whopping fibs about where they have been for the last seven years. They say they have been down the Nile river (but they won't go down the water-chute at the swimming pool). Or uncles say they can fly an aeroplane (but they can't even fly a kite).

Uncles have terrible table manners. They suck up spaghetti and splatter you with tomato sauce. They eat custard with their fingers and wipe their hairy moustaches with the tablecloth.

SURPRISE NUMBER TWO

Being told you have a new baby brother or sister. The good news is that Mum and Dad will be so busy looking after the baby that you can do what you want! The bad news is that they will soon be so tired that you'll have to do all the washing-up and tidying up.

Here is some more good news and bad news:

Hooray! Mum and Dad will buy lots of new toys.
Boo! The toys will be babyish.

Hooray! Gran and Grandpa will visit.
Boo! They will spend all day going 'ga ga' to the baby.

Hooray! You will have someone to play football with.
Boo! All babies do is dribble!

A new baby in the house will get a lot of fuss. You may feel left out. If you do:

a) remember that grown-ups made a fuss of you as well (trouble is, you were too young to remember).

b) remember that mums and dads still love you (even if they spend all day talking about the baby).

Seven things parents say about babies

'He has got his grandad's ears.'
'He's got his dad's hair.'

'He's got your bedroom!'
'She is only a week old and she can walk/talk/ fly a space shuttle.'
'It's your turn to change the nappy.'
'She's just like her mum/gran/sister.'
'No! You can't swop her for a puppy.'

SURPRISE NUMBER THREE

Getting something through the letter box.
Grown-ups are sent rotten things like gas bills through the letter box, which is why they groan *(they should be called 'groan-ups' – Ed).*

Seven-year-olds are sent nice things like postcards, or letters from pen pals.

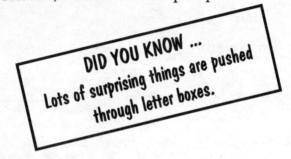

DID YOU KNOW ...
Lots of surprising things are pushed through letter boxes.

● Local newspapers.

Great if you want to do papier mâché models, or want to read about what is going on in your town. Local newspapers do not have very exciting news. On the front page it will say, 'Hamster escapes from pet shop' or 'Seven-year-old boy cleans his shoes'.

● Tiny packets of free washing-up liquid.

Lots of free things are pushed through the letter box. Trouble is, they are not things that seven-year-olds want. If you do get sent something good like a free bar of chocolate it

is the size of a
postage stamp
(and tastes like one
as well). You never
get sent a free bike
or a free television.

● <u>Birthday cards.</u>

It is lovely to get a birthday card. Sometimes
grannies put money in the envelope (an old
penny or sixpence). If your granny does send
you a birthday card with a twenty-pound
note inside then the card will

a) get lost in the post, or

b) be sent next door by mistake.

Grans and grandpas never remember how
old you are. (They never remember how old
they are either!) So you will get a birthday
card with a badge which says:

Top tip: Grannies and grandads have very wobbly writing. As they get older their writing gets wobblier.

SURPRISE NUMBER FOUR

Being told you are going to move house.
Someone once worked out that you move into a home every seven years or so (unless you are a snail).

Some grown-ups move because they want a bigger house with a larger garden. Other grown-ups move because they want a smaller house with a tiny garden. If you have grotty neighbours you might want to move away from their noise.

If you move into a new house you may have to go to a new school because your old school is too far away. If you have moved away from your friends it is not all bad news because you can still be pen pals! Plus, you will soon make new friends at your new school. Don't worry too much about moving house. Snails do it all the time!

Top tip: *How to get the biggest (and best) bedroom:* Brothers and sisters will have big rows about where they are going to sleep. They will be very loud and drive Mum and Dad crazy. Do not join in. Go up to your parents and tell them that you don't mind getting the smallest bedroom (even if you do). Your mum and dad will think you are very unselfish and give the biggest and best room to **you**. (Watch out they don't give you the smallest room and keep the nicest room for themselves. Grown-ups are like that!)

How to make sure you take everything with you:

Go round the house and make a list of everything that is yours.

Put all the things you've listed into cardboard boxes to stop them breaking on the journey to your new house. Write what is in the box on the outside of the box (so if you need a toy in a hurry you won't have to open every box to find it). Put clothes and toys you use the most at the top of the box (so they are easy to get out if you need them).

Before you pack everything away why not take a photo of your bedroom? Then you will know where everything goes when you unpack. And you will have a photo to remind you of your 'old' room.

MUMS AND DADS

Parents are full of surprises!

1) They keep changing their hairstyles.

Monday Wednesday

2) They keep changing their cars.

3) They keep changing their promises.

4) They keep changing their moods.*

Every **seven-year-old** knows that mums and dads have two moods:

*GOOD MOODS AND BAD MOODS

Mums and dads take turns so when Mum is in a good mood Dad is in a bad mood. Then when Dad is in a good mood Mum is in a bad mood.

This can be very useful because if you ask Dad for some sweets and he says 'NO!' you can go and ask Mum ... who will say 'Yes' because she is in a good mood.

You can tell when Dad is in a bad mood because he will:

a) have a black rain cloud above his head.

b) go and sit in the car and listen to loud music.

c) sit in the front room and listen to his terrible music (and be told off by Mum because it is TOO LOUD!).

Dads get in bad moods when:

a) you beat them at chess or snap.

b) you leave food on the side of your plate.

c) they are told *they* have left food at the side of their plates.

d) they have had a rotten day at work.

e) you have eaten the last packet of crisps.

f) mums tell them to go to the shop (to buy a new packet).

You know when Dad is in a good mood because he will:

a) give you extra pocket money.

b) pick food you don't like off the side of your plate.

c) let you watch cartoons when his favourite T.V. show is on.

Dads get in good moods when:

a) you give them a card on Father's Day.

b) you give them the last packet of crisps.

c) their football team has won.

d) you let them win at chess.

You can tell when Mum is in a bad mood because she will:

a) say 'KEEP THE NOISE DOWN!' very loudly.

b) make lots of cups of tea.

c) knit a scarf in about seven seconds.

d) fold her arms and give you a hard stare!

Mums get in bad moods when:

a) you say 'Is tea ready?' every two seconds.

b) big sisters come in late and don't say where they have been.

c) you take ages to get ready for school.

d) dads cut their toenails in the front room.

You can tell when Mum is in a good mood because she will:

a) let you wear the clothes you want.

b) let you stay up.

c) let your seven friends stay for tea.

Mums get in good moods when:

a) dads buy them flowers.

b) you get a good school report.

c) you remember their birthdays.

d) you are nice to grotty brothers and sisters.

Seven things that make seven-year-olds groan

1. Mum licks her fingers and wipes your face.

2. Dad throws you up in the air like a football.

3. Big brothers pinch money from your piggy bank.

4. Teachers give you a surprise spelling test.

5. Mum won't let your best friend stay the night.

6. Your best friend's mum won't let you stay the night.

7. Your friend has a secret and won't tell you what it is.

EVERYTHING YOU NEED TO KNOW ABOUT SECRETS

(SSSHHH...BUT DON'T TELL ANYONE!)

We all keep secrets. Write down your most secret secret here:

Which of these things would you keep a secret?

○ Your teacher has a wig.

○ You got 0 in your spelling test.

○ You have a silly-looking swimming cap.

○ You don't like chips.

○ Your twin brother or sister is an alien.

○ You have eaten a dog biscuit.

○ You have eaten two dog biscuits.

○ Your mum ties your shoelaces. *barking mad*

○ You can juggle.

○ Your dad talks to his car.

○ Your middle name.

chomp

Tick ✓ the ones you would keep a secret.

How to keep secrets secret

Never tell bothers and sisters your secrets because they can't keep a secret. So if you tell them you are afraid of the dark they will have told the WHOLE WORLD this secret in about seven seconds.

Only tell a secret to a friend if your friend has told you a secret. If your friend then tells someone your secret then you can tell someone else their secret (*sounds very complicated – Ed*).

If you want to write your secret down then use invisible ink. Look in this box and see if you can read the secret message.

"THERE IS NO WRITING IN THIS BOX – FOOLED YOU!"
If you can't see any writing in this box then here is what the message is:

It's easy to make your own invisible 'inks' using lemon juice, cola or milk. Just squeeze lemon juice (or pour cola or milk) into a saucer and use a cotton bud or lolly stick to write your message. When you want to see what you have written put the paper on top of a warm radiator so the 'ink' dries. (You can also ask a grown-up to put the paper in a warm oven to dry.)

1. You can use wax crayons to write hidden messages too. Just rub a piece of paper with a white wax crayon.

2. Turn it over and put it on top of a white sheet of paper.

3. Write your message (press down hard) and give the bottom sheet to a friend.

4. Your friend now tips coffee powder on to the paper and gives it a shake so the secret message appears.

(How? Well, the coffee powder sticks to the wax writing that was made when you pressed through the top sheet.)

Why not be super-sneaky and hide your message in a shopping list, or an old birthday card? Don't forget to write with 'invisible ink'.

tomato onion peas chocolate comflakes	tomato Dear Sam onion meet me at my house peas and make sure your chocolate sister does not follow you comflakes

MIRROR WRITING

It is fun if you write a message that can only be read if you look at it in a mirror:

a mirror→

It's a bit of a secret that a few words do not change or look funny when you see them in a mirror:

(How? Well some letters of the alphabet are symmetrical and look the same when they are turned around, like: H I C O E D.)

SECRET CODES

Here is a secret code that is very tricky to crack.

You will only be able to work out the message using this grid:

ABC	DEF	GHI
JKL	MNO	PQR
STU	VWX	YZ

The code (secret message) says, **'I am seven.'** Can you work out how it is done?

There are lots of ways to send secret messages to your pals. One of the best ways to send a message is to use **Morse Code.**

Morse Code was invented in 1838 by an American called Samuel F.B. Morse. It's a dotty way to dash off a message. Each letter or number is made of dots, dashes or dots and dashes.

A dot looks like this • *and a dash looks like this* -
The alphabet is written:

A • - **B** - ••• **C** - • - • **D** - • • **E** •

F •• - • **G** - - • **H** •••• **I** •• **J** • - - -

K - • - **L** • - •• **M** - - **N** - • **O** - - -

P • - - • **Q** - - • - **R** • - • **S** ••• **T** -

U •• - **V** ••• - **W** • - - **X** - •• - **Y** - • - -

Z - - ••

81

You would write the word 'SECRET' like this,

```
•••      •      - • • •     • - •      •         -
 S       E        C          R        E         T
```

Morse Code is simple to write, and if anyone asks you what you are writing tell them your pen is leaking!

Secret Sentences!

You can be a slippery customer and hide secret words inside sentences. If you are secretly about to visit a country called Canada you could write, '_Can Adam_ come out to play today?'

Enemy spies (like big brothers) will not know about the hidden word. Test your friends with these sentences. Can they find the seven hidden animals?

1. I will see my sister at two o'clock.

2. Do gob-stoppers last a long time?

3. You must come in now or Mum will be mad!

4. My cut knee was full of bad germs.

5. I grab bits of snow and make a snowball.

6. I am well and smiling or ill and frowning.

7. The flower in the pot was pretty.

(Answers: rat, dog, worm, badger, rabbit, gorilla, wasp)

Seven-year-olds like to keep secrets. Some strange creatures and mysterious places also have their own secrets. To find out more, read on, if you dare!

1. STONEHENGE (in Wiltshire, England)

is a circle of giant stones. The stones are about four metres tall, and have other stones laid on top:

Inside the main circle there is another ring of stones. The stones have come from many kilometres away (perhaps Wales) and no one knows how they were moved. Some scientists say that the stones are a very early type of calculator. People used them to work out when, for instance, there would be an eclipse.

Top tip: Why not make your own Stonehenge out of breakfast cereal?

2.THE LOST CITY OF ATLANTIS

This city is a bit of a mystery. No one knows where the lost city of Atlantis is because it's ... er ... lost. Some people say it was built by some people who were the cleverest people in the world. One day the city was destroyed by the sea which swallowed it up. (If they were so brainy why did they build it so near the sea?) An Ancient Greek writer called Plato wrote all about Atlantis and since then lots of people have tried to find it. Some experts say it might be underwater near a place called Crete. No one is really sure.*

Top tip: If you go for a paddle by the seaside watch what you tread on.

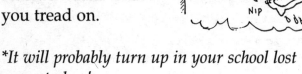

It will probably turn up in your school lost property box!

3. EASTER ISLAND

In the Pacific Ocean there is a place called Easter Island. It is a small island and it got its name because it was discovered on Easter Day (in 1722). The island is dotted with very large stone heads, over three metres tall. They look like Dad when you bury him in the sand.

These stone statues were carved inside a volcano, and then put all over the island. No one knows why they were made. *(Perhaps they are fossilised Easter eggs? – Ed.)*

4. THE LOCH NESS MONSTER

Loch Ness is a lake in Scotland. The Loch Ness monster (Nessie) was seen about 1,500 years ago by St. Columba. Since then it has been sighted many times.

Some people think Nessie looks like

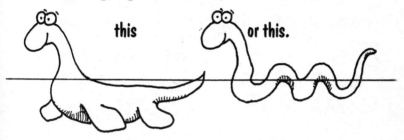

this   or this.

No one knows what the monster is, but Nessie could be a *plesiosaur*, a *pliosaur* or an *ichthyosaur*.

The Loch Ness monster is protected by Scottish law just in case it exists.

OF COURSE I EXIST!

5. THE YETI

The Yeti is said to be a big hairy creature that lives in Asia, in the Himalayan mountains.

You have probably seen big hairy creatures walking around on two legs in your school. They are not Yetis. They are teachers.

The Yeti has a loud roar and smells funny (so do teachers – Ed). It is protected, like Nessie, even though no one has proved that the Yeti exists ... yet!

There are lots of mysteries in this world. Perhaps you know the answers to these ones?

▶ Why do new shoes always hurt your feet?

▶ Why can't grown-ups open child-proof bottles?

▶ Why do dads have hairy ears and noses?

▶ Why can't we cure a cold?

▶ Why do dads wash the car just before it rains?

▶ Why do seven-year-olds have earlobes?

EVERYTHING YOU NEED TO KNOW ABOUT SECRET AGENTS!

Secret agents can do lots of things secretly. They can walk down streets and not be seen. They do not tell anyone what they do and they like to wear a disguise so you can't see who they are!

Look at this picture. Can you spot the secret agent?

Did you guess right?

Secret agents have to stop crooks taking over the world. These crooks are in charge of gangs with silly names like P.L.O.P. or S.P.L.O.S.H. (Secretly Planning Lots Of Horribleness).The crook in charge usually loves cats and hates secret agents.

If you want to be a **seven-year-old** secret agent you will have to invent a secret identity so that no one knows your real name, or who you really are.

Name: Ivor Secret

Address: 007 Bond Street,
London

Age: 8 years old

Height: It's a secret

Weight: So is this

Hobbies: Following people around, usually Mum (oops that should be a secret!)

Favourite clothes: Any clothes I don't wear to school

Favourite saying: " My name's Secret. Ivor Secret"

Favourite food: Minced (s)pies

Seven-year-old secret agents must take a secret promise. If you want to be a secret agent then please read the promise and sign your name.

'I, Secret Agent Number Seven, promise to stop anyone naughty from trying to take over a) the school b) the world c) the T.V. remote controls.

I will do my best to rescue anyone, or anything, in trouble. Including beastly brothers, snotty sisters, or spiders that get stuck in the sink!'

Signed by...

Super secret agents wear cunning disguises so that even their best friends do not know who they are. Try shaking talcum powder on your head to make it look white, or coffee powder to make it go brown. (Make sure you wear a hat if you go outside in case it rains.)

The Secret Agent Disguise Kit *

Guaranteed to fool someone very stupid!

89

You can also make yourself look different by combing your hair the wrong way, or sticking rice crispies on your face to make it look like you have got warts. If you have a teenage sister borrow her black lipstick and black-out a few of your teeth.

Good secret agents blend into the background:

They have special gadgets too.

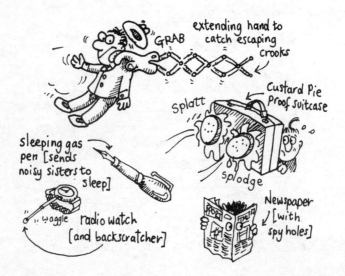

If you want to talk to another secret agent then make this terrific telephone!

You will need 2 clean yoghurt pots and a piece of string (3 metres long).

1. Ask a grown-up to help you make a hole in the bottom of both the yoghurt pots.

2. Tie a knot in one end of the string.

3. Thread the string through one of the holes, and then through the hole in the other pot.

4. Tie a knot in this end too.

5. Give your friend one pot. Move apart so that the string is pulled tight.

6. Speak into the pot and when you want to hear your friend put the pot to your ear!

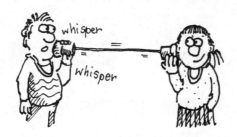

You can send messages without talking.
Why not send secret signals like these?

ACTION	SECRET MESSAGE	WHAT OTHER PEOPLE THINK
1. scratching chin	= yes	you have an itchy chin
2. scratching nose	= no	you have an itchy nose
3. tying shoelace	= someone is looking at you	your shoelace is undone
4. coughing	= I am being watched	you have a cough
5. one sneeze	= meet me in the shed	you have a cold
6. two sneezes	= meet me in the shop	you have a bad cold
7. three sneezes	= meet me at school	you have a very bad cold

PUZZLING PRINTS

If you look at the skin on your fingertips you
will see lots of tiny lines. These lines make a
print if you press your fingertips on an inky
pad and then on to paper.

You will not have the same fingerprint as
another person. They are always different.
Secret agents can look at fingerprints left after
a crime and track down who made them.

Fingerprints do not change. If you make a
fingerprint while you are seven, keep it for 63
years and make a new print when you are 70,
you will see that both prints look the same.

Fingerprints do make patterns.

THE WHORL   THE ARCH   THE LOOP   THE COMPOSITE

The Whorl has lines that go round, a bit like water when it goes down a plug hole. The Arch has an arch shape, just like a hill. The Loop bends over like Grandad when he picks up the paper. The Composite can be a mixture of Loops, Whorls or Arches.

YOUR FINGERPRINTS

To see what your fingerprints look like,

a) Eat a sticky chocolate cake using your fingers. Then press your sticky fingers here:* *(Not a good idea - Ed).*

b) Fold up a piece of tissue paper and put it on a plate. Squeeze a few drops of ink out of an ink cartridge onto the paper. Press your fingers on the inky tissue and then make fingerprints here:

RIGHT HAND

thumb   helix (pointing) finger 2nd finger 3rd finger   little finger

LEFT HAND

*WARNING! Do not leave prints on the cake tin.

c) If you don't want to make a lot of mess then rub lipstick on your fingers, or wax shoe polish (much better idea – Ed).

Top tip: If you want to make a really good print then roll your finger from side to side as you press it down on the paper. For more fingerprint fun why not make fingerprint animals?

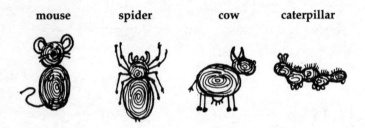

| mouse | spider | cow | caterpillar |

Why not take prints of all your family and then look at them with a magnifying glass?

FINGERPRINT TRAIL: to find out if anyone has left a trail of fingerprints in your house you will need:

- talcum powder
- a fine paint brush
- clear sticky tape
- drinking chocolate
- scissors

What you do

Sneak around the house looking for fingerprints. If you find a fingerprint on something dark:

1. Dip your brush in talcum powder.

2. Brush the powder gently on to the fingerprint.

3. Blow the powder off the print (or wipe it off with a clean brush).

4. Now cover the print with sticky tape.

5. Press it down and peel it off gently.

You will have a fingerprint on the tape. Stick the tape on dark paper and it will show up.

If you see a print on something light then dust it with chocolate powder, or lead from a pencil.

Now you can find out who has been in your bedroom, or who has been pinching your sticky sweets!

MISSION IMPOSSIBLE

A secret agent has to go on dangerous missions (jobs). Imagine that you (Secret Agent Number 7) are being sent on a mission. You have to travel to seven countries. Your boss, Mrs ZZZZZ, has mixed the letters of each country into a crazy code!

Now you have to crack the code and work out which countries you are going to go to:

GOOD LUCK!
You have seven minutes and seven clues.

- This country looks like an old boot   TLAYI   _ _ _ _ _
- This is a very nice land!   CNDALIE   _ _ _ _ _ _ _
- You might eat this at Christmas   UKERTY   _ _ _ _ _ _
- Sounds a bit fishy to me   WASEL   _ _ _ _ _
- Wrap up warm, it sounds cold here   CHEIL   _ _ _ _ _
- I was late for school so I did this   RNIA   _ _ _ _
- Any germ   GRMNAYE   _ _ _ _ _ _ _

Some missions are impossible. For instance,
MISSION 7
CODE NAME: CREAM CAKE
Mission Objective: to creep downstairs late at night and take a cream cake from the fridge before your dad/brother/sister eats it.

Deadly Dangers:

1. The fridge light may be seen by grown-ups.

2. Grown-ups might come in the kitchen just as you open the fridge door.

3. You may bump into a brother or sister on the same mission.

4. You could leave a trail of incriminating evidence (crumbs!).

Success Rating: *Impossible*

Reason?: A grown-up will have eaten the cake as soon as you went upstairs to bed.

What to do if spotted by the enemy:

a) say you were sleepwalking **RR** 🌳🌳

b) say you were about to wash up the dishes as a nice surprise **RR** 🌳🌳🌳

c) say you are on a top secret mission and cannot tell anyone what it is, or your ham-ster/slug/earwig's life is in terrible danger **RR** 🌳

RR (rhubarb ratings)

🌳 = you might get away with it

🌳🌳🌳 = your story won't wash so you'll
end up washing the dishes

🌳🌳🌳🌳 = no chance of getting away
with it

SECRET FEELINGS

When babies are sad they go red like a tomato
and cry. When they are happy they gurgle
and smile a lot.

If they do not feel happy they will do this:

SPLODGE

Have you ever felt sad and not told anyone? Have you been given a toy that you didn't want and said, 'It's lovely' when you thought it was yukky?

Sometimes we hide our feelings because we don't want to upset anyone.

If you feel mad it is a good idea to let off steam like a kettle:

kettle (boiling madly) **seven-year-old (boiling mad)**

You can let off steam by kicking a football, skipping, or having a long swim. Some **seven-year-olds** go to the bottom of the garden and yell their heads off (yuk! – Ed). Some talk to their teddies (or write a letter to Gran).

Why not write about your feelings?
Onions make me cry.
Pollution makes me sad.
Dad makes me laugh.
Birthdays make me feel happy.

One way to make yourself feel happy is to go and cheer up someone else. You can tell them a story, do a job for them, or tell some jokes!

Sometimes you do not need to say anything, you just have to listen.

BULLIES

Bullies like to call kids names and push them around. They bully because they feel they can get away with it. Some bullies secretly want to be nice but they do not know how to make friends. This makes them feel miserable so they pick on smaller or younger kids.

If a bully makes you feel sad *tell a grown-up or friend*. If you stand up to a bully then the bully will go away.

SECRET THOUGHTS

Some seven-year-olds secretly think about:

● *what they want to be when they grow up*

When you leave school you could be a chef and cook lots of nice food (hooray) but everyone else gets to eat it (boo). You could be a doctor and make people better (hooray). Trouble is, you could catch their grotty germs (boo)! You could become a school teacher (hooray) but you'd have to go to school for ever and ever!

● who they want to sit next to

Some seven-year-olds end up sitting next to kids who fiddle with things (like pencils or ... their nose) or copy their work. Teachers never let you sit next to your best friend because they think you will gossip or mess about (true!). If you want to sit next to your best friend then here is what to do:

At the start of the year go into the class-room and pretend that you and your pal have never met before. Say things like, 'What is your name?' to your friend, or 'Are you new, because I have never seen you before?'

Your teacher will think that you are strangers and let you sit together for the rest of the year! Hooray!

● what it would be like to fly

It would be fun if seven-year-olds could flap their arms and fly like birds. Sadly, birds have hollow bones and big muscles and seven-year-olds don't.

Ancient Greeks loved to make up myths (stories) about people who could fly.

Here is the sad (but untrue) story of *Daedalus and Icarus.*

Daedalus was a very clever man who was famous for building the Minotaur's Maze on the island of Crete. One day, Daedalus and the King of Crete had a row and Daedalus was locked in a tall tower with

101

his son, Icarus.

It wasn't very nice in the tower so Daedalus decided to escape. He secretly made some wings then Daedalus and Icarus flew out of their prison over the sea. Daedalus told his son not to fly too close to the sun. Unfortunately, Icarus was a bit of a high flier and did not listen to his dad's warning. Sad to say, the wax on his wings melted and all his feathers fell off!

Icarus plunged into the sea like a stone and was seen no more. Daedalus flew to the island of Sicily and lived happily ever after, even though his arms ached for weeks.

SECRET WISHES

Some seven-year-olds wish to know where Mum hides all their birthday presents. Other seven-year-olds wish they could swop their sisters for a guinea-pig. If you have any secret wishes write them here. (Remember to use invisible ink!)

-
-
-
-

EVERYTHING YOU NEED TO KNOW ABOUT CREEPY CRAWLIES

The world is full of creepy crawlies. There are millions of different creepy crawlies which is why you always get covered in them when you go on a picnic!

CREEPY CRAWLIES AT HOME

Creepy crawlies wriggle all over the house. Many creepy crawlies are pests and the biggest pest looks like

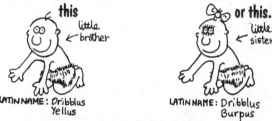

this
little → brother
LATIN NAME: Dribblus Yellus

or this.
little → sister
LATIN NAME: Dribblus Burpus

These creepy crawlies get EVERYWHERE!!! They can move dead fast even though they are small. If you chase them they will hide behind the sofa or in the dog basket.

HOW TO FIND THEM

You will never find babies washing up, tidying their bedrooms, or taking the dog for a walk. You always know when a little baby is around because seven seconds after they have gone into a room it will look **A MESS!**

before a baby came
into the room

seven seconds after

It is easy to see where little brothers and sisters have been because they leave things behind them:

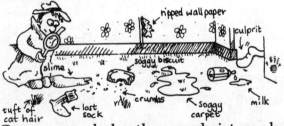

Creepy crawly brothers and sisters always vanish when it is time for bed, or when they have got to have a bath. They like making funny noises and funny smells (*cor – what a pong – Ed*).

They sleep quietly for most of the day, but as soon as you go to bed they will make lots of noise and keep everyone awake. Still, creepy crawly brothers and sisters do have some good points.

● You can help them eat their ice-creams.

● If you break something you can say they did it.

● You can dress them up in your old baby clothes (to see how silly you looked).

● None of your bigger brother's grotty pals like to visit when creepy crawlies are around.

● None of your bigger sister's spotty boyfriends like to visit when creepy crawlies are around.

● Creepy crawly brothers and sisters are nice to cuddle when your teddy is in the wash.

Sadly, they have some bad points too:

● If they break something you get the blame.

● They never have to clean up the mess they make (but you have to).

● They are too young to buy you a present, and will break all yours.

Three things NEVER to say to a creepy crawly baby

1. *'Put that down'*

Babies think everything they pick up is theirs (so do teachers who confiscate your toys). Babies don't care if it is Gran's best teapot or your best clothes that they are grabbing.

A creepy crawly baby will put everything in its mouth.

When they get bored they will throw things into the bin, or over you.

When they give you your things back they are soggy with dribble!

2. *'I wish you could walk'*

A creepy crawly baby will crawl everywhere. They like to grab the cat's tail, or put things in the video machine.

If they could walk they would go into your bedroom, or into your secret camp in the garden. Even worse, they will follow you everywhere. Even when you go to the loo! They are like pets (except pets don't have tantrums when they can't get their own way).

WARNING! Creepy crawly babies are terrors when they start to walk. They are more terrible than 'burnt fish cakes' and 'soggy chips'.

3. *'Would you like a drinky-winky?'*
Don't say this because your pals might hear you and giggle like mad. Soppy mummies and sloppy aunties love to say words like 'drinky-winky'. These words are not cool! Here are some more 'baby' words that seven-year-olds should **NEVER** say (and what they mean).

'**din dins**' = dinner
'**choo choo**' = train
'**moo moo**' = cow
'**piggy wiggy**' = pig

'**toothy-pegs**' = teeth
'**beddy-byes**' = bedtime
'**baa baa**' = sheep
'**yum yum?**' = is it nice?

Write here any soppy words that grown-ups have said to you!

Creepy Crawly Camera Snaps

You were once a creepy crawly (*it's true! – Ed*).
WARNING! Mum will have lots of yukky
photos of you ... just like these!

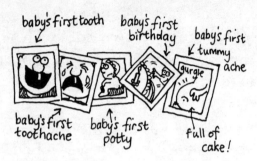

baby's first tooth
baby's first birthday
baby's first tummy ache
gurgle
baby's first toothache
baby's first potty
full of cake!

CREEPY CRAWLY CREATURES

*Creepy crawly creatures are everywhere. They are
quite easy to spot if you keep your eyes peeled, and
know where to look.*

Perhaps the creepiest of crawlies are **insects**.
There are hundreds of thousands of different
kinds. Here are just a few (that live very near
you!).

AUNTS

An aunt likes to pop round to your house
once a year. They bring lots of presents.
Aunts have hairy chins and shiny red
lipstick. Aunts are ... (*You are meant to be
talking about ants – Ed.*)

Sorry.

ANTS

Ants can be seen running in the garden, or
the sugar bowl, looking for tasty things to
eat. There are over 6000 kinds of ant. Small
red ants and larger black ants often live in the
same garden. Beware! Red ants will bite you
if you get too close, and their bite **STINGS!**

Some ants look after herds of aphids and
'milk' them to produce 'honeydew' milk. It is
sweet and sticky and fit
for a Queen. Other ants
spend all their time
looking after the Queen!

OH NO! WE FORGOT
THE MILK!

EARWIGS

Earwigs have scary looking pincers which look
v. scary, but won't harm you. If you look at an
earwig closely you won't see little wigs on their
ears. This is because they fall off when it is
windy!

Earwigs love funny jokes. This is their best
joke of all:
What did the earwig say as it jumped off the wardrobe?
Earwigo again!

Earwigs mainly come out at
night. During the day they
hide under stones and bark.

WOOF

BOMBADIER BEETLES

This beetle loves to chomp up other insects. When it is frightened it jets out a puff of liquid and makes a LOUD BANG. This scares off any attackers. Bombadier beetles hide in Christmas crackers and go bang when you pull them.

BEES

Bees were named after the second letter of the alphabet. They come in all shapes and sizes. Some bees have funny names. The carpenter bee loves to do lots of sawing and woodwork.

The honey bee builds a nest using wax from its own body. Honey bees carry pollen on their hind legs and make honey from the sticky stuff (nectar) they find in flowers. They are called honey bees because they fly about calling everyone 'Honey'.

Bumble bees are quite rare. Some bumble bees think they are the bees knees because they are so large (2 to 4 cm). They have bright yellow stripes which warn you to keep away from their sting. Bumble bees like to bumble

around the garden (like Grandpa when he
looks for his specs).

A bumble bee
sometimes likes to live
underground, in an old
mouse hole.

CLICK BEETLES

These beetles live in grassland or hedgerows.
They get their name because when they fall
on their backs they turn themselves the right
way up with a loud **CLICK!**

SEVEN SPOT LADYBIRDS

They are found in lots of places, and can be
seen in the garden for most of the year. These
ladybirds have a red body and black spots
when they are fully grown. Young seven spot
ladybirds are blue with yellow spots!
Ladybirds are a kind of beetle. *(They are not
birds – Ed.)* Some ladybirds have up to 22
spots *(still not as many as spotty teenagers – Ed)*.

LADYBIRD GAME

Here is a fun game that knocks the spots off
other games. You have to try to be the first
player to draw a ladybird.

You will need: paper, pencils, dice and lots of friends.

How to play: ask all the players to throw the dice. The first player to get a six then starts. This player throws again, trying to throw a '**1**'.

'**1**' = the body '**3**' = the legs '**5**' = the antennae

'**2**' = the head '**4**' = the eyes '**6**' = the spots

You need to throw a '**1**' because you have to draw the body first. Then you can add the other pieces. Don't forget to draw the head before you draw the eyes, '4', and the antennae, '5'. The player who draws this ladybird first is the winner.

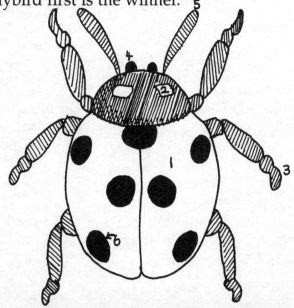

QUICK QUIZ:

Look at this list of batty beetle names. Put
X by the ones that you think are made up.*

Jewel beetle ☐   Stag beetle ☐

Oil beetle ☐   Tortoise beetle ☐

Furniture beetle ☐   Bloody-nosed beetle ☐

Great Diving beetle ☐   Soldier beetle ☐

Mum, I've got a nose bleed again

FLIES

A fly is brilliant at flying. If it was brilliant at
running it would have been called a RUN. If
it was a fantastic jumper it would have been
called a JUMP. *(Are crickets called CRICKETS
because they are good at playing cricket? – Ed.)*

Flies are cleverer than you think. Some flies
wear a disguise and make it look like they are
bees. They even lay their eggs in bees' nests.
While hover-flies look just like wasps, the
scorpion-fly has a tail like a deadly scorpion.
It looks scary but this fly wouldn't hurt a fly.
There isn't a sting at the end of its tail.

Flies like to eat lots of different things. The

Amazingly – all these beetles really exist!

113

horse-fly rides on horses and sucks up blood
for dinner. *(Perhaps it should be called the
Hoover fly? – Ed.)* The sneaky robber-fly grabs
insects in mid-air. Then it drags them to the
ground and eats them. The house-fly flies
around your house sucking up runny food,
like custard or gravy. Some flies are very
noisy and give you a headache. The
bluebottle is very noisy and gives itself a
headache!

All flies have terrible table manners. They
spread germs and diseases (like malaria).
You must clean anything that a fly has
crawled on because flies never wipe their
feet before they come indoors.

CATERPILLARS

Caterpillars can creep over all sorts of things.
They don't mind walking on leaves upside-
down. Caterpillars are always hungry and
love eating cabbage. When you are eating
school dinners always check your cabbage
to make sure there isn't a caterpillar hiding
underneath.

Caterpillars do not all look the same.

Some look like hairy eyebrows.

Some look like bird droppings.

A few caterpillars have hairs that make you itch or give you a rash if you touch them. The hairs stop birds and school cooks taking caterpillars away for dinner. The Australian hawkmoth caterpillar waves its bottom at birds who want to eat it. Here's why:

| Caterpillars have up to five pairs of false legs. TRUE ☐ or FALSE ☐ ? | * |

In Mexico there are plant seeds that look like beans. Inside each bean is a baby caterpillar. When the sun warms up the bean the caterpillar inside begins to jump and jerk. This makes the bean jump around as if by magic.

Caterpillars change into butterflies or moths by becoming a pupa with a hard case (chrysalis). The caterpillar's body then cleverly turns into soup. A month later a butterfly or moth squeezes out of the hard case, soggy and wrinkled (like you when you've been in the bath too long). When its wings have dried out it flies away.

MAKE YOUR OWN CREEPY CATERPILLAR

You will need: 2 pipe cleaners, sticky tape, pencil, round lids, 2 lolly sticks, cardboard (from an old cereal box), paper fasteners.

1. Draw and cut out one large circle, five smaller circles, and two very small circles (draw around three different-sized lids). Ask a grown-up to put small holes in the large circle and the five smaller ones.

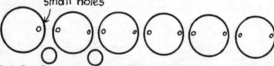
small holes

2. Stick the two smallest circles on to the largest one. Then colour them in to look like eyes. You have now finished making the caterpillar's head.

paper fastener

3. Join the rest of the circles together with paper fasteners to make the body. Colour them in and glue on short pieces of wool to make the body look hairy. Fix the head on to the body with a paper fastener.

4. Tape a lolly stick onto each end and two pipe cleaners on to the head.

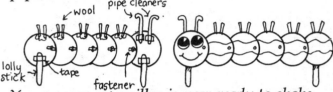

Your creepy caterpillar is now ready to shake, rattle and roll!

CREEPY CRAWLY JOKES

Why do bees have sticky hair?
Because they use honeycombs

How do bees go to work?
By buzz

Which insect is always the best at school?
The tick

What is the definition of a worm?
A caterpillar with no clothes on

What do you get if you cross a spider with a washing machine?
A spin dryer

What's black and yellow and flies, backwards?
An eeb

What do you call a spider with no legs?
A currant

What do you call a fly when it retires?
A flew

WHERE TO FIND CREEPY CRAWLIES

● on the front row next to the teacher (school swots and teacher's pets).
● on tree trunks (hawk moths and goat moths).
● under bark (Queen wasps, beetles – cardinal beetles, bark beetles, the longhorn beetle).
● on leaves and stems (leaf hoppers, ladybirds, frog hoppers, caterpillars – peacock butterfly caterpillar, yellowtail moth caterpillar).
● in the house (lacewings, silverfish).
● on walls (butterflies – wall brown butterfly).
● rubbish heaps (dung beetle, house cricket).

- in the soil (turnip moth caterpillar, wire worms, worms).
- under stones (earwigs, garden tiger moth, bristletails: these are like brown silverfish).

If you want to know more about these creepy crawlies then why not visit your local library or ask your teacher to let you do a project on them.

CREEPY CRAWLIES AT SCHOOL!

There are crawly creeps who NEVER fidget, play with rulers or giggle when they see the teacher's new haircut. They stay behind after school to tidy up the classroom, and when they grow up they want to be teachers, worse luck!

When they put their hands up they are always right! Teachers can tell they know the answer because kids always answer questions in three ways:

knows the answer   not sure   hasn't a clue

If you put two hands up and wiggle them about, your teacher will think you need to go to the bathroom ... ahem.

THE RETURN OF THE MAGNIFICENT SEVEN

(More seven facts to amaze your friends)

● The marsh frog weighs just over seven ounces (200 grams). The Goliath frog can weigh over seven pounds. (3.3 kilograms).

● The 'Seven Years War' lasted from 1756 to 1763.

● The number seven is 'sept' in French, 'sette' in Italian and 'sieben' in German.

● The name 'Asong' means seventh born.

● Albatross chicks take about seven days to break out of their tough eggshells.

● The Pacific Ocean in one place is over seven miles (11 kilometres) deep.

● Some dinosaur eggs weigh about seven kilograms. The Pentaceratops (pent-ah-ser-a-tops) dinosaur's body was seven metres long.

● The Seven Wonders of the World are:

1. The Pyramids of Giza in Egypt (built by some old geezer!).

2. The Hanging Gardens of Babylon (built by Nebuchadnezzar, King of Babylon, in 600 BC).

3. The Statue of Zeus, at Olympia in Greece – which was 12 metres tall.

4. The Temple of Diana, at Ephesus (Turkey) – which was built in the third century BC.

5. The Tomb of Mausolus, at Halicarnassus – which was destroyed by an earthquake.

6. The Colossus of Rhodes. This was a bronze statue of Helios (God of the Sun) made from melted bronze instruments and weapons.

7. The Pharos at Alexandria – which was a great lighthouse built around 280 BC. It was destroyed by an earthquake in 1375 AD.

EVERYTHING YOU NEED TO KNOW ABOUT TOYS AND GAMES

Seven-year-olds have always loved playing with toys and games. Sadly, brothers and sisters have always loved borrowing them and not giving them back. When you do lend toys they end up

a) in big pieces

b) in small pieces

c) with someone else's name on!

BALL GAMES have been popular, ever since the Ancient Egyptians played 'catch' with clay balls filled with beads. When they were thrown in the air they made a noise. If they hit you on the head you'd make a noise too!

Egyptian seven-year-olds also played with spinning tops, and wooden toys with wheels. One Ancient Egyptian game called 'Nine Men's Morris' is over 3000 years old. The Romans liked to play 'Tabula'. This game is

still being played today *(must be a long game –*
Ed). Nowadays we call it 'Backgammon'.

The Vikings (who came from Norway,
Sweden, Finland and Denmark) played board
games when they were bored of raiding and
fighting other countries. They played
'Hnefatafl' (also called 'Halatafl') which is hard
to say but easy to play. In the game the King is
attacked and has to be saved by his men. They
also played 'Merils' which is a bit like
'Draughts'.

GAMES FROM LONG AGO.

● 'Chess' comes from India and is like a very
old game called 'Chaturanga'.
● 'Snakes and Ladders' was first played in
India, where it was called 'Moksha-Patamu'.
● 'Dominoes' has been played
in China since 1120 AD. A
Domino is a winter hood worn
by a priest. It is black on the
outside and white on the inside, just like *dominoes*.

white inside

black on the
outside

● Playing cards have been around for over 700
years. Old cards from Italy didn't have *spades*,
clubs, *diamonds* and *hearts* on them. Instead,
they had *cups*, *swords*, *clubs* or *coins*.
● Seven-year-olds in Ancient Greek times
played with yo-yos.

The Ancient Greeks had a great game called **FIVESTONES**. To play it you will need five stones! An Ancient Greek called Aristophanes wrote about the game, over 2000 years ago!

There are lots of ways to play **FIVESTONES**.

Here is one of them:

1. Hold five stones in your hand. Throw them up and see how many you can catch on the back of your hand.

2. Pass the stones to a friend who does the same thing. *Whoever catches the most stones wins.*

The Romans loved to play with 'knucklebones' (anklebones of sheep!) or 'hucklebones' (pigs' trotters !!). A modern version of the game is called 'Jacks'.

GIANT STEPS is an old British game. It is also called 'Mother May I?' or 'Father May I?' *How to play:* stand at one end of a room and pretend to be Mum or Dad. Get your pals to stand at the other end. You then tell one of your friends to do something, such as **'Take one Giant Step'**.

The player has to ask, 'May I?' before moving. Then you say, 'yes' or 'no'. Any player who forgets to say, 'May I?' has to go back to the start. If you say 'no' you then tell the person to do something else, like **'Take three baby steps'**. And your friend must ask, 'May I?' again.

All players, one at a time, get a go. They also try to sneak forward without asking Mother or Father's permission. If they are spotted by you they go back to the start.

Here are some things you can tell your friends to do:

'Do a banana split' (slide your foot in front of you as far as you can).

'Do an umbrella step' (spin like a dancer and step forward with your hand on your head).

'Do a bunny hop' (half crouch down and do a little jump forward).

'Do a frog jump' (crouch down and jump forward as far as you can).

'Blind step' (walk forward with eyes shut).

The first player to get to Mother or Father (you) wins. Why not invent some steps?

TAG was invented a long time ago. We know that in Ancient Rome a man called Horace used to watch kids race around tagging (touching) each other. The best player was 'rex eris' (made the king). Tag was also played a lot when Elizabeth I was Queen of England.

It's not fair! I want to be made the queen!

Ahem... You are the queen!

The simple game of tag goes like this. The boy or girl who is 'it' has to run around trying to tag (touch) someone. Everyone tries to run away. If you are tagged then you are now 'it' and have to run after someone else.

There are lots of other ways to play:

Floating Tag: you are safe if you have both feet off the ground. So you can't be tagged if you are on a chair with your feet up in the air.

Iron Tag: you are only safe when you are holding on to something made of metal, like a lamp post, or a fence.

Stone Tag: you are safe if you are touching something made of stone, such as a wall, or a stone!

Spotlight Tag: (*my favourite – Ed*) you play this in the dark with a torch. The player who is 'it' tries to shine a beam of light on you. If the beam 'hits' you then you become 'it'.

Shadow Tag: if the player who is 'it' jumps on your shadow then you become 'it'. No touching is allowed.

TERRIBLE TOYS

Some seven-year-olds are given terrible toys. They hide them in the wardrobe or shed (so their pals will not see them!). Can you remember any terrible toys?

My worst toys are

....

....

Many mums and dads keep their terrible old toys because they were given to them by someone special (like Granny or Grandpa). Or because the toys bring back happy memories of when they were seven. (Yes – all grown-ups were once seven years old!)

TOY COLLECTING

Some grown-ups like to collect old toys, e.g.

dolls   clockwork toys   lead soldiers *

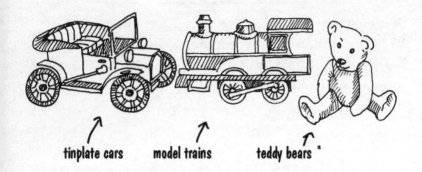

tinplate cars   model trains   teddy bears *

* King Louis XIII of France collected toy
soldiers. His collection was worth **LOTS** of
money. He gave the soldiers to his son,
also called Louis (Louis XIV), who used
them to plan real wars and battles.

* Teddy bear toys are collected by people all
over the world. The first teddy bears are
worth **LOTS** and **LOTS** of money because there
are not many left. They look like real bears,
with long snouts (noses) and long legs.
   Teddy bears are named after a US President
called Theodore Roosevelt
(1858-1919) who was nicknamed 'Teddy'.

'How does a Teddy Bear get to school?'
'On a bearcycle'

128

TEDDY BEARS

are terrific because:

1. they keep you nice and warm in bed.

2. they don't take your sweets without asking.

3. they don't call you silly names.

4. they won't cry if they fall out of bed.

5. they are lovely to cuddle up to.

6. they never sulk if you don't want to play with them.

7. they are not afraid of the dark! Some teddies lose fur or an eye, but it does not matter what they look like. They are always there for you to hold, day or night.

Many dads are loopy about train sets. You can tell how loopy they are by the shape of the train track.

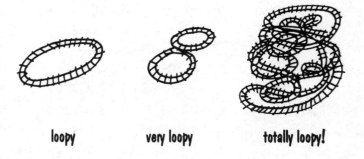

loopy   very loopy   totally loopy!

HOW TO GET THE TOY YOU HAVE ALWAYS WANTED

1. Eat lots of sweets so all your teeth fall out. Put them under your pillow and hope the tooth fairy comes in the night.

2. If you need a bit more money to buy your toy then try this sneaky trick. Put a piece of sweetcorn under your pillow. The tooth fairy will think it's a yellow tooth and give you some money for it.

YOU CAN'T FOOL ME!

sweetcorn

3. Do lots of jobs for Mum and Dad in return for some extra pocket money. It's a good idea to do jobs that they don't want to do. Offer to

- *tidy your bedroom* £
- *wipe the dishes* £
- *weed the garden* ££
- *polish Dad's shoes* £££
- *water the plants* £
- *clean inside the car* ££

£ = grotty   *££ = very grotty*   *£££ = grottiest job of all*

4. Be an angel. Say 'please' and 'thank you' to Granny. Smile at your neighbours. Give your baby brother or sister a hug (wash your hands afterwards!). With luck, your mum and dad will give you a toy for being so nice!

130

DODGY TOYS

If you had a dodgy apple with a worm inside you would not want to eat it. Some toys are dodgy too.

loose button [might choke you]

sharp hidden spike

frayed wire [could shock you]

pencil rubbers [could choke if put in mouth]

stuffing that is not fire resistant [or flameproof]

look v. tasty [worse luck]

SOLO GAMES

Here are seven great things for you to do when your friends can't come over to play.

1. *Get your tongue in a twist with tricky tongue-twisters.* Can you say seven tongue-twisters seven times without stopping, or mixing up the words.

three tree twigs
red lorry, yellow lorry
she sells seashells
Bill's back brake block broke
five fresh fried French fries
elastic plastic
sooty sheets

2. *Hunt for seven-letter words in a dictionary.* In seven minutes, write down as many seven letter words as you can.

3. *Try to walk across a room in exactly seven minutes.* If you are too fast, or too slow, you have to start again.

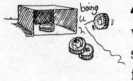

4. *Try to get coins in a box.* You will need seven coins and a small box. Put the box on the floor and try to roll all seven coins into it. If this is too easy then stand further away from the box.

5. *Make words out of your name.* Write your name on a piece of paper and then see how many smaller words you can make. If this is too easy you are not allowed to make two letter words (at, in, of, so).

6. *Crafty coin-catching.* Bend your right or left arm so that your elbow is in the air and the back of your hand is by your shoulder. Straighten your arm quickly and catch as many coins as you can. Start with one coin. (*Can you catch seven? – Ed.*)

7. *Spot the sevens.* Look around your bedroom. Try to spot seven things that start with the letter 'A'. Then find seven things that begin with 'B'. See if you can get all the way to 'Z'.

MAKING YOUR OWN TOYS

Puppet toys have been around for over 2,500 years. You see, smart seven-year-olds in Ancient Greece used to play with puppets made from clay, wood or bone.

Why not make some of your own puppets, using old wooden spoons, squeezy bottles and paper bags?

Why not build a puppet theatre using an old cardboard box? You can then make up stories and get your puppets to act out the words.

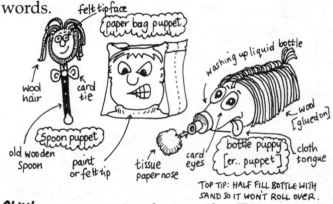

felt tip face
paper bag puppet
washing up liquid bottle
wool hair
card tie
Spoon puppet
old wooden spoon
paint or felt tip
tissue paper nose
card eyes
wool [glued on]
bottle puppy [er.. puppet]
cloth tongue

TOP TIP: HALF FILL BOTTLE WITH SAND SO IT WON'T ROLL OVER.

Skittles are very simple to make. Take six empty squeezy bottles (make sure they are not full of washing-up liquid). Cover them with paper and paint each skittle a bright colour. If you like why not stick on some silver or gold stars?

bottle
glue
paper

133

Now stand the skittles up (about three metres away) and try to knock them down with a tennis ball (or a rolled-up old sock). Score a point for every skittle that you knock over. If the skittles fall over too easily then put some sand or marbles in them.

JUNK TOYS

Every house has lots of junk in it. You can make great toys out of junk. Why not be canny and make a pair of stilts ? Or make music with margarine tubs?

WARNING!

Always use *junk*. **NEVER** play hockey with Gran's walking stick, or turn Mum's expensive pearl necklace into a set of marbles!

FAVOURITE GAMES OF
SEVEN-YEAR-OLDS

BANGER

All you need: some friends, a few buttons and a wall.

Give all your friends one button. You start the game by putting a button near a wall. The other players each take a turn to throw their button against the wall. If a player's button drops within one hand span of the button on the floor then it counts 2 points. If it is within two hand spans then it counts 1 point.

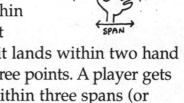

If a player's button hits the button on the floor (and it lands within one hand span) then it counts four points. If it lands within two hand spans then it counts three points. A player gets one point if it lands within three spans (or over). First to score seven points wins.

BULLIHEISLE

All you need: a few friends.

Ask your friends to join hands and stand in a straight line. Stand at one end of the line and let your friend at the other end wind

135

everyone around you. Then your friend has to 'unwind' everyone. This game is also called 'Wind Up Jack'.

FIND THE RING

All you need: string, a ring and lots of friends.

Get your friends to sit in a circle, holding a long piece of string with a ring threaded on it. You have to stand in the middle of the circle and close your eyes. Count to seven while your friends secretly pass around the ring. When you open your eyes you have to guess who is holding the ring. If you are right you swop places with that person.

COBBLERS

All you need: balloons, string, marker stones and some friends.

Each player has a piece of string and ties a balloon to one end of it. The other end is tied to the player's wrist. Mark out a square playing area using four stones, and then get everyone to stand inside it. Now try to burst the other balloons but don't let anyone burst your balloon. The game ends when there is only one player still left holding a balloon. You must not go out of the playing area.

It is more fun if the balloon is tied to your ankles and partly filled with water.

AND FINALLY: THINGS YOU HAVE DONE WHILE YOU'RE SEVEN

- I washed up the dishes.
- I made a cake.
- I told my best friend a secret.
- I stayed in bed because I was ill.
- I gave Mum a flower.
- I learned my telephone number off by heart.
- I did not watch television for a day.
- I had an indoors picnic.
- I washed behind my neck.
- I ate a school dinner (and survived).
- I put a tooth under my pillow.
- I told my teacher a good joke.
- I carried some shopping without dropping or eating it!
- I swam at least five metres.
- I looked after a plant.
- I washed the car.
- I read a comic from cover to cover.
- I sneezed with my eyes open.

If you like, you can list all the other 'fab firsts' you have done while you're seven:

●

●

●

●